The
"FOREVER
FRIENDS"
Book
for
Mum

by Deborah Jones.

First published in 1991
by Brownsword Books
28 Gay Street, Bath, England

Printed and bound in Great Britain by
William Clowes Limited, Beccles and London

ISBN 1 873615 00 0

To Mully

from

?

EĖΩNA

for My Mum, June.

To _____

from _____

Mum knows you're
never too big for
a Hug !

There is no friend
to equal your mother

A Mother always
listens ..... with her
Heart!

Mothers give the most precious gift of all .....

...their love!

Mother holds your hand,
when you are little, ...

..... and your Heart, forever !

When You need advice,
 One way or the other,
 Don't decide what to do
 until you've asked Mother!

When you're feeling blue....

Mum always knows what to do !

Mothers think of all the
little things that show
how much they care.

All Mums
are wonderful ....

..... but my_mum is best of all !

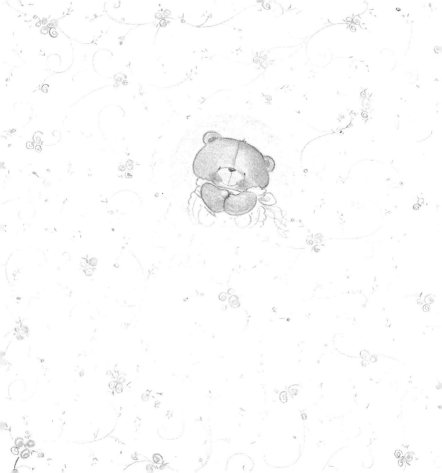